Ascension:
Out of the Ashes
A Journal of Self-Discovery and Empowerment

This journal belongs to:

_____

🌐 http://www.movitajohnsonharrell.com/
http://thecharlesfoundation.com/

ISBN:978-1737913-7-02

Published by Virtual Way Professional Services

Introduction

In my book Pheonix Arising, I shared so much of my life; my ups and downs, from my addiction to my fall from grace. Many of those downs I did to myself and in other instances, it was at the hands of others.

I also shared how I was able to rise from the ashes of my firey life. God planted a seed of purpose in me and no matter what happened to me, I had supernatural strength to keep rising even in the most difficult situations, like losing both of my precious sons to the ugliness of gun violence.

I also shared how I was able to rise from the ashes of my firey life. God planted a seed of purpose in me and no matter what happened to me, I had supernatural strength to keep rising even in the most difficult situations, like losing both of my precious sons to the ugliness of gun violence.

I have come to realize that more than the therapy, the medication, and the gift of faith, the key to my being able to keep going is Gratitude. Even on my worst day, I am able to rise up because I am grateful for my life, my husband, and my family.

This journal is designed to help you discover the things you are grateful for in your life. Let it bless you and cause you to ascend in your own life and lead you on a path to self-discovery and empowerment. . Rise up and be Grateful!

Movita Johnson-Harrell

There's always another level up.
There's always another ascension.
More grace, more light, more
generosity, more compassion,
more to shed, more to grow.

-Elizabeth Gilbert

Date: _____

Upon My Rising

Affirmation

I am grateful for:

_____
_____
_____
_____
_____
_____
_____
_____
_____
_____
_____
_____
_____
_____
_____
_____
_____
_____
_____

Today I am looking forward to:

_____
_____
_____
_____
_____
_____

At the Setting of my Day

Today was great because:

_____
_____
_____
_____
_____
_____
_____
_____
_____

I am grateful for:

_____
_____
_____
_____
_____
_____
_____
_____
_____

End of day reflections

_____
_____
_____
_____
_____
_____
_____
_____

Notes

Date: _____

Upon My Rising

Affirmation

I am grateful for:

_____
_____
_____
_____
_____
_____
_____
_____
_____
_____
_____
_____
_____
_____
_____
_____
_____

Today I am looking forward to:

_____
_____
_____
_____
_____

At the Setting of my Day

Today was great because:

_____
_____
_____
_____
_____
_____
_____
_____
_____

I am grateful for:

_____
_____
_____
_____
_____
_____
_____
_____

End of day reflections

_____
_____
_____
_____
_____
_____
_____
_____
_____

Notes

Date: _____

Upon My Rising

Affirmation

I am grateful for:

_____
_____
_____
_____
_____
_____
_____
_____
_____
_____
_____
_____
_____
_____
_____
_____
_____
_____
_____

Today I am looking forward to:

_____
_____
_____
_____
_____
_____

At the Setting of my Day

Today was great because:

_____
_____
_____
_____
_____
_____
_____
_____
_____

I am grateful for:

_____
_____
_____
_____
_____
_____
_____
_____
_____

End of day reflections

_____
_____
_____
_____
_____
_____
_____
_____

Notes

Date: _____

Upon My Rising

Affirmation

I am grateful for:

_____
_____
_____
_____
_____
_____
_____
_____
_____
_____
_____
_____
_____
_____
_____
_____
_____
_____
_____

Today I am looking forward to:

_____
_____
_____
_____
_____

At the Setting of my Day

Today was great because:

_____
_____
_____
_____
_____
_____
_____
_____
_____

I am grateful for:

_____
_____
_____
_____
_____
_____
_____
_____

End of day reflections

_____
_____
_____
_____
_____
_____
_____
_____
_____

Notes

Upon My Rising

Affirmation

_____

I am grateful for:

_____
_____
_____
_____
_____
_____
_____
_____
_____
_____
_____
_____
_____
_____
_____
_____
_____
_____

Today I am looking forward to:

_____
_____
_____
_____
_____
_____

At the Setting of my Day

Today was great because:

_____
_____
_____
_____
_____
_____
_____
_____
_____

I am grateful for:

_____
_____
_____
_____
_____
_____
_____
_____
_____

End of day reflections

_____
_____
_____
_____
_____
_____
_____
_____
_____

Notes

Date: _____

Upon My Rising

Affirmation

I am grateful for:

_____
_____
_____
_____
_____
_____
_____
_____
_____
_____
_____
_____
_____
_____
_____
_____

Today I am looking forward to:

_____
_____
_____
_____
_____

At the Setting of my Day

Today was great because:

_____
_____
_____
_____
_____
_____
_____
_____
_____
_____

I am grateful for:

_____
_____
_____
_____
_____
_____
_____
_____
_____
_____

End of day reflections

_____
_____
_____
_____
_____
_____
_____
_____
_____

Notes

Date: _____

Upon My Rising

Affirmation

I am grateful for:

_____
_____
_____
_____
_____
_____
_____
_____
_____
_____
_____
_____
_____
_____
_____
_____
_____
_____
_____
_____

Today I am looking forward to:

_____
_____
_____
_____
_____
_____

At the Setting of my Day

Today was great because:

_____
_____
_____
_____
_____
_____
_____
_____

I am grateful for:

_____
_____
_____
_____
_____
_____
_____
_____

End of day reflections

_____
_____
_____
_____
_____
_____
_____

Notes

Date: _____

Upon My Rising

Affirmation

I am grateful for:

_____
_____
_____
_____
_____
_____
_____
_____
_____
_____
_____
_____
_____
_____
_____
_____
_____

Today I am looking forward to:

_____
_____
_____
_____
_____

At the Setting of my Day

Today was great because:

_____
_____
_____
_____
_____
_____
_____
_____
_____
_____
_____

I am grateful for:

_____
_____
_____
_____
_____
_____
_____
_____
_____
_____
_____

End of day reflections

_____
_____
_____
_____
_____
_____
_____
_____
_____
_____
_____

Notes

Date: _____

Upon My Rising

Affirmation

I am grateful for:

_____
_____
_____
_____
_____
_____
_____
_____
_____
_____
_____
_____
_____
_____
_____
_____
_____

Today I am looking forward to:

_____
_____
_____
_____
_____

At the Setting of my Day

Today was great because:

_____
_____
_____
_____
_____
_____
_____
_____
_____

I am grateful for:

_____
_____
_____
_____
_____
_____
_____
_____
_____

End of day reflections

_____
_____
_____
_____
_____
_____
_____
_____

Notes

Upon My Rising

Affirmation

I am grateful for:

_____
_____
_____
_____
_____
_____
_____
_____
_____
_____
_____
_____
_____
_____
_____
_____
_____

Today I am looking forward to:

_____
_____
_____
_____
_____

At the Setting of my Day

Today was great because:

_____
_____
_____
_____
_____
_____
_____
_____
_____

I am grateful for:

_____
_____
_____
_____
_____
_____
_____
_____

End of day reflections

_____
_____
_____
_____
_____
_____
_____
_____
_____

Notes

Date: _____

Upon My Rising

Affirmation

I am grateful for:

_____
_____
_____
_____
_____
_____
_____
_____
_____
_____
_____
_____
_____
_____
_____
_____
_____
_____
_____
_____

Today I am looking forward to:

_____
_____
_____
_____
_____

At the Setting of my Day

Today was great because:

_____
_____
_____
_____
_____
_____
_____
_____
_____

I am grateful for:

_____
_____
_____
_____
_____
_____
_____
_____

End of day reflections

_____
_____
_____
_____
_____
_____
_____
_____

Notes

Date: _____

Upon My Rising

Affirmation

I am grateful for:

_____
_____
_____
_____
_____
_____
_____
_____
_____
_____
_____
_____
_____
_____
_____
_____
_____

Today I am looking forward to:

_____
_____
_____
_____
_____

At the Setting of my Day

Today was great because:

_____
_____
_____
_____
_____
_____
_____
_____
_____

I am grateful for:

_____
_____
_____
_____
_____
_____
_____
_____
_____

End of day reflections

_____
_____
_____
_____
_____
_____
_____
_____
_____
_____

Notes

Upon My Rising

Affirmation

I am grateful for:

_____
_____
_____
_____
_____
_____
_____
_____
_____
_____
_____
_____
_____
_____
_____
_____

Today I am looking forward to:

_____
_____
_____
_____
_____
_____

At the Setting of my Day

Today was great because:

_____
_____
_____
_____
_____
_____
_____
_____

I am grateful for:

_____
_____
_____
_____
_____
_____
_____
_____

End of day reflections

_____
_____
_____
_____
_____
_____
_____
_____

Notes

Date: _____

Upon My Rising

Affirmation

I am grateful for:

_____
_____
_____
_____
_____
_____
_____
_____
_____
_____
_____
_____
_____
_____
_____
_____

Today I am looking forward to:

_____
_____
_____
_____

At the Setting of my Day

Today was great because:

_____
_____
_____
_____
_____
_____
_____
_____
_____
_____

I am grateful for:

_____
_____
_____
_____
_____
_____
_____
_____
_____

End of day reflections

_____
_____
_____
_____
_____
_____
_____
_____

Notes

Date: _____

Upon My Rising

Affirmation

I am grateful for:

_____
_____
_____
_____
_____
_____
_____
_____
_____
_____
_____
_____
_____
_____
_____
_____
_____
_____
_____

Today I am looking forward to:

_____
_____
_____
_____
_____

At the Setting of my Day

Today was great because:

_____
_____
_____
_____
_____
_____
_____
_____

I am grateful for:

_____
_____
_____
_____
_____
_____
_____
_____

End of day reflections

_____
_____
_____
_____
_____
_____
_____
_____

Notes

Date: _____

Upon My Rising

Affirmation

I am grateful for:

_____
_____
_____
_____
_____
_____
_____
_____
_____
_____
_____
_____
_____
_____
_____
_____
_____
_____
_____

Today I am looking forward to:

_____
_____
_____
_____
_____

At the Setting of my Day

Today was great because:

_____
_____
_____
_____
_____
_____
_____
_____
_____
_____

I am grateful for:

_____
_____
_____
_____
_____
_____
_____
_____
_____

End of day reflections

_____
_____
_____
_____
_____
_____
_____
_____
_____
_____

Notes

Date: _____

Upon My Rising

Affirmation

I am grateful for:

_____
_____
_____
_____
_____
_____
_____
_____
_____
_____
_____
_____
_____
_____
_____
_____
_____
_____
_____

Today I am looking forward to:

_____
_____
_____
_____
_____

At the Setting of my Day

Today was great because:

_____
_____
_____
_____
_____
_____
_____
_____
_____

I am grateful for:

_____
_____
_____
_____
_____
_____
_____
_____
_____

End of day reflections

_____
_____
_____
_____
_____
_____
_____
_____
_____

Notes

Date: _____

Upon My Rising

Affirmation

I am grateful for:

_____
_____
_____
_____
_____
_____
_____
_____
_____
_____
_____
_____
_____
_____
_____
_____
_____

Today I am looking forward to:

_____
_____
_____
_____
_____

At the Setting of my Day

Today was great because:

_____
_____
_____
_____
_____
_____
_____
_____
_____
_____

I am grateful for:

_____
_____
_____
_____
_____
_____
_____
_____
_____

End of day reflections

_____
_____
_____
_____
_____
_____
_____
_____
_____
_____

Notes

Upon My Rising

Affirmation

I am grateful for:

Today I am looking forward to:

At the Setting of my Day

Today was great because:

_____
_____
_____
_____
_____
_____
_____
_____
_____

I am grateful for:

_____
_____
_____
_____
_____
_____
_____
_____
_____

End of day reflections

_____
_____
_____
_____
_____
_____
_____
_____
_____

Notes

Upon My Rising

Affirmation

I am grateful for:

_____
_____
_____
_____
_____
_____
_____
_____
_____
_____
_____
_____
_____
_____
_____
_____
_____
_____

Today I am looking forward to:

_____
_____
_____
_____
_____

At the Setting of my Day

Today was great because:

_____
_____
_____
_____
_____
_____
_____
_____
_____

I am grateful for:

_____
_____
_____
_____
_____
_____
_____
_____
_____

End of day reflections

_____
_____
_____
_____
_____
_____
_____
_____
_____

Notes

Date: _____

Upon My Rising

Affirmation

I am grateful for:

_____
_____
_____
_____
_____
_____
_____
_____
_____
_____
_____
_____
_____
_____
_____
_____
_____
_____

Today I am looking forward to:

_____
_____
_____
_____
_____

At the Setting of my Day

Today was great because:

_____
_____
_____
_____
_____
_____
_____
_____

I am grateful for:

_____
_____
_____
_____
_____
_____
_____
_____

End of day reflections

_____
_____
_____
_____
_____
_____
_____
_____

Notes

Date: _____

Upon My Rising

Affirmation

I am grateful for:

_____
_____
_____
_____
_____
_____
_____
_____
_____
_____
_____
_____
_____
_____
_____
_____
_____

Today I am looking forward to:

_____
_____
_____
_____
_____

At the Setting of my Day

Today was great because:

_____

_____

_____

_____

_____

_____

_____

_____

_____

_____

I am grateful for:

_____

_____

_____

_____

_____

_____

_____

_____

_____

End of day reflections

_____

_____

_____

_____

_____

_____

_____

_____

Notes

Date: _____

Upon My Rising

Affirmation

I am grateful for:

_____
_____
_____
_____
_____
_____
_____
_____
_____
_____
_____
_____
_____
_____
_____
_____
_____

Today I am looking forward to:

_____
_____
_____
_____
_____

At the Setting of my Day

Today was great because:

_____

I am grateful for:

_____

End of day reflections

_____

Notes

Date: _____

Upon My Rising

Affirmation

I am grateful for:

_____
_____
_____
_____
_____
_____
_____
_____
_____
_____
_____
_____
_____
_____
_____
_____

Today I am looking forward to:

_____
_____
_____
_____

At the Setting of my Day

Today was great because:

_____

_____

_____

_____

_____

_____

_____

_____

_____

_____

I am grateful for:

_____

_____

_____

_____

_____

_____

_____

_____

_____

End of day reflections

_____

_____

_____

_____

_____

_____

_____

_____

_____

Notes

Date: _____

Upon My Rising

Affirmation

I am grateful for:
_____
_____
_____
_____
_____
_____
_____
_____
_____
_____
_____
_____
_____
_____
_____
_____
_____
_____

Today I am looking forward to:
_____
_____
_____
_____
_____
_____

At the Setting of my Day

Today was great because:

_____
_____
_____
_____
_____
_____
_____

I am grateful for:

_____
_____
_____
_____
_____
_____

End of day reflections

_____
_____
_____
_____
_____
_____
_____

Notes

Date: _____

Upon My Rising

Affirmation

I am grateful for:

_____
_____
_____
_____
_____
_____
_____
_____
_____
_____
_____
_____
_____
_____
_____
_____
_____
_____

Today I am looking forward to:

_____
_____
_____
_____
_____

At the Setting of my Day

Today was great because:

_____
_____
_____
_____
_____
_____
_____
_____
_____
_____

I am grateful for:

_____
_____
_____
_____
_____
_____
_____
_____
_____

End of day reflections

_____
_____
_____
_____
_____
_____
_____
_____
_____

Notes

Upon My Rising

Date: _____

Affirmation

I am grateful for:

_____
_____
_____
_____
_____
_____
_____
_____
_____
_____
_____
_____
_____
_____
_____
_____
_____
_____

Today I am looking forward to:

_____
_____
_____
_____

At the Setting of my Day

Today was great because:

_____
_____
_____
_____
_____
_____
_____
_____

I am grateful for:

_____
_____
_____
_____
_____
_____
_____
_____

End of day reflections

_____
_____
_____
_____
_____
_____
_____
_____

Notes

Upon My Rising

Affirmation

I am grateful for:

_____
_____
_____
_____
_____
_____
_____
_____
_____
_____
_____
_____
_____
_____
_____
_____
_____
_____

Today I am looking forward to:

_____
_____
_____
_____
_____

At the Setting of my Day

Today was great because:

_____
_____
_____
_____
_____
_____
_____
_____
_____
_____

I am grateful for:

_____
_____
_____
_____
_____
_____
_____
_____
_____

End of day reflections

_____
_____
_____
_____
_____
_____
_____
_____
_____

Notes

Date: _____

Upon My Rising

Affirmation

I am grateful for:

_____

_____

_____

_____

_____

_____

_____

_____

_____

_____

_____

_____

_____

_____

_____

_____

_____

_____

_____

Today I am looking forward to:

_____

_____

_____

_____

_____

At the Setting of my Day

Today was great because:

_____
_____
_____
_____
_____
_____
_____
_____
_____

I am grateful for:

_____
_____
_____
_____
_____
_____
_____
_____

End of day reflections

_____
_____
_____
_____
_____
_____
_____
_____

Notes

Upon My Rising

Affirmation

I am grateful for:

_____
_____
_____
_____
_____
_____
_____
_____
_____
_____
_____
_____
_____
_____
_____
_____
_____
_____

Today I am looking forward to:

_____
_____
_____
_____
_____
_____

At the Setting of my Day

Today was great because:

_____
_____
_____
_____
_____
_____
_____
_____
_____
_____

I am grateful for:

_____
_____
_____
_____
_____
_____
_____
_____

End of day reflections

_____
_____
_____
_____
_____
_____
_____
_____

Notes

Date: _____

Upon My Rising

Affirmation

I am grateful for:

_____
_____
_____
_____
_____
_____
_____
_____
_____
_____
_____
_____
_____
_____
_____
_____
_____
_____

Today I am looking forward to:

_____
_____
_____
_____
_____

At the Setting of my Day

Today was great because:

_____
_____
_____
_____
_____
_____
_____
_____
_____

I am grateful for:

_____
_____
_____
_____
_____
_____
_____
_____

End of day reflections

_____
_____
_____
_____
_____
_____
_____
_____

Notes

About the Creator

Movita Johnson-Harrell is a wife, mother, grandmother, and author. She is an activist and author that fights to empower those most marginalized.

As the Executive Director of MECA, for over two decades she has advocated, cared for and fought to improve the quality of life for disenfranchised groups

Movita's youngest of four children, Charles Andre Johnson, 18 years old was shot and killed in a case of mistaken identity. In April of 2011 after Charles' murder, Movita created the CHARLES Foundation, (**Creating Healthy Alternatives Results in Less Emotional Suffering**) Since implementing the foundation Movita has worked nationally to protect and empower our youth and to address the social determinants that lead to gun violence.

On March 12th, 2019 Movita won the special election for State Representative for the 190th legislative district and made history as the first Muslim woman ever elected to the General Assembly in Pennsylvania.

On March 5th, 2021, Movita's surviving son, Donte' L. Johnson, 30 years old, was shot and killed in a random drive-by while on a trip to California. Movita' continues to work in the memory of both of her sons Donte' and Charles. She works to address the social determinants that lead to gun violence, including systemic racism, poverty, and gentrification.

Made in the USA
Middletown, DE
25 September 2021